Strategic Faith

Workbook

Lucy Ann Costa-Quattrone

Published by LucyAnnCQ Enterprises
914 Brookcrest Arch, Chesapeake, VA. 23320

Author's Bio Picture Credit: Luanne Dietz

ISBN: 978-1-64184-691-2

Available in paperback and digital
Printed in the United States of America

Table of Contents

Welcome

*I'm so glad you have chosen Strategic Faith for your group
or personal faith development journey.*

*It is possible to experience life connected to God in a world moving
far from Him. It is possible to move from religion to relationship,
and to set your mind on all that is good and trustworthy.*

*The purpose of this workbook is to help you engage in a partnership with
God to uncover your created greatness. You will emerge from struggle to
strength and uncertainty to trust as you embrace living a life beyond
limitations. We will accomplish this by engaging in a three-part process:*

1. Uncovering the Struggle
2. Undertaking the Shift
3. Unleashing the Strategies

*I encourage you to spend time each week praying about and exploring the concepts
in each lesson. My hope is that through prayerful thought and honest self-evaluation,
(along with open discussions with your group or mentor if applicable), you will
learn how to strategically use your faith to transform your life—impacting the
relationships you have, the work you do, and the world you live in.*

Here's to harnessing the power of Strategic Faith and reclaiming your greatness!

Lucy Ann

How to use this workbook

➤ *Each part of this study starts with specific objectives designed to enhance your experience.*

➤ *Every action step is designed to bring you to a place of thought. Embrace whatever time is necessary to honestly reply—there are no wrong answers. Be encouraged to use a journal to make note of the things the Lord reveals to you along the way. (Often, the space provided will be insufficient.) This is your journey with God—keeping record of all He reveals to you is a priceless gift.*

➤ *You are encouraged to select relevant Bible passages each week and write them on index cards. This is how you will build your Bible deck. Keep this deck of cards handy for easy access. Reference it consistently to help bring you comfort, peace, and support, on your journey to greatness.*

➤ *Much of your relationship with God happens in prayer. Be encouraged to end each week's session with a time of prayer. Look back over what you have studied each week. Consider your areas of strengths and weaknesses. Decide what you desire to take to God in prayer.*

➤ *Enjoy the journey!*

* *Unless otherwise noted, all Bible references are from the NIV.*

The Journey Begins Now & The Struggle

Faith Is the Pathway to Greatness
Ignorance Devours

Recommended Reading
Strategic Faith Book, pages 1-5 & chapter 1

Session 1

The Journey Begins Now

Faith Is the Pathway to Greatness

Objectives

As a result of exploring **Faith Is the Pathway to Greatness**, you will learn to…

➤ open your heart and mind to the possibility of the greatness that lies within
➤ understand faith to be the key to unlocking your created greatness
➤ free yourself from the bondage of living a good life and take hold of the promise of an abundant life
➤ set yourself on a pathway to greatness, empowered by faith, to live a life beyond limitations

1. Describe what faith means to you?

2. In this section we learn that faith is God's strategic design to give you an upgrade in every area of your life. How are you being challenged to see your faith through a different lens? Write about it.

3. In what way does faith play a role in your everyday life?

4. On pages 2 & 3 we see several key points about the struggles we face in life and how faith plays a role in our journey to greatness. Review these—take note and list any areas that are roadblocks for you. In doing so, you will be positioning yourself to overcome these obstacles in the future.

5. Why do you think God places such an emphasis on faith?

6. On page 4, we are asked to consider a deep question. *If Jesus were here in the flesh, walking beside you right now, would you alter your daily routine?* How would you respond?

7. There are many scriptures about faith in the Bible. Below are a few. Look them over, choose which ones inspire you, and add them to your Bible deck. If you have others that are your favorites add them as well.

2 Corinthians 5:7
For we live by faith, not by sight.

James 1:6
But when you ask, you must believe and not doubt, because the one who doubts is like a wave of the sea, blown and tossed by the wind.

John 11:40
Then Jesus said, "Did I not tell you that if you believe, you will see the glory of God?"

Hebrews 11:6
And without faith it is impossible to please God, because anyone who comes to him must believe that he exists and that he rewards those who earnestly seek him.

8. Take a moment and evaluate where you are on your faith journey. There's no right or wrong answer. Honesty will help you move forward without any self-judgment.

9. Before proceeding any further, now is the time to make a commitment to see this journey through to the end. Write a letter of commitment to yourself. In doing so, you are declaring that seeking God, listening to His voice, and obeying Him, are priorities in your life.

Here are a few things to consider when you write your commitment letter:

- ✓ What do you most want to learn in this study?
- ✓ Why is this important to you?
- ✓ How will you prioritize your time to do the necessary work to achieve your goals for this study?

Here's an example of a commitment letter. Feel free to use this or create your own. Be sure it is handwritten, signed, and dated. Make it personal.

I give myself permission to be open to whatever God has for me on this journey. I commit to being honest with myself and with God, allowing the Holy Spirit to lead, guide, and direct my path—illuminating the steps before me with His love. My heart is open and my mind is ready to receive. I want to draw closer to God and develop a personal relationship with Him. I want to go from struggle to strength and uncertainly to trust as I connect with God on a deeper level. I plan to prioritize this study by completing each lesson, engaging with my study group, online community, and mentor, so I may grow and help others on their journey as well.

Write your commitment letter here

The Struggle

Ignorance Devours

Objectives

As a result of exploring **Ignorance Devours**, you will learn to...

> ➤ openly and honestly examine the foundations of your belief system and the degree to which these govern your life
> ➤ identify if your faith is rooted in religious theology or based upon a personal relationship with God as Father
> ➤ pinpoint to what extent ignorance may have played a role in sabotaging the growth of your faith

1. On page 10 we see an example of how *the lens of religion* can skew a person's perspective about who God is. In what way can you relate? How has religion played a role in defining your relationship with God?

2. What religious concepts have you blindly accepted that may be holding you back from entering into a closer relationship with God?

3. On page 14, we read—*There is a God who has placed within every person a longing to be in constant fellowship with Him, and there is an enemy whose sole purpose is to prevent that from happening.* In what way have you experienced this tug-of-war in your own heart?

4. The Bible is full of references to wisdom. Explore the following and pick those that resonate with you. Write them down and add them to your Bible deck.

Proverbs: 3:13
Blessed are those who find wisdom, those who gain understanding.

Proverbs: 4:6
Do not forsake wisdom, and she will protect you; love her, and she will watch over you.

Proverbs: 16:16
How much better to get wisdom than gold, to get insight rather than silver!

Proverbs 19:8
The one who gets wisdom loves life; the one who cherishes understanding will soon prosper.

Remember, much of your relationship with God happens in prayer. Look back over what you have studied this week. What things will you bring to God in prayer? Reflect and write your prayer on the following page.

Reflection Page

Session 2

The Struggle

Yesterday's Pain Is a Trap
Doubt and Unbelief Are Ambushes
Battle Fatigue Is Real

Recommended Reading
Strategic Faith Book, chapters 2-4

Session 2

The Struggle

Yesterday's Pain Is a Trap

Objectives

As a result of exploring **Yesterday's Pain Is a Trap**, you will learn to…

➢ recognize how past hurts are creating limitations for you today
➢ identify areas of your heart where you have built a secret cave of protection
➢ trust your wounded heart to God

1. On page 15, we learned that the pain of yesterday can leave us gasping for breath today. God wants you to breathe freely. What memories still bring you pain today? List them here.

2. Can you identify any emotions that came to the surface regarding the memories you listed? (Anger, guilt, shame, etc.) These are limiting you from living in freedom. Acknowledging them is necessary to overcome their power to control you any longer.

3. If you are ready, talk to God about these hurts—tell Him how you are feeling. Write down what you hear God saying to you in this process. If you are unable to do this—what do you think must happen for you to take this leap of faith and bring these hurts to God?

4. Below are Bible verses to encourage you in overcoming heartache. Pick the ones that are particularly meaningful to you—add them to your Bible deck.

Psalm 147:3
He heals the broken hearted and binds up their wounds.

Proverbs: 15:13
A happy heart makes the face cheerful, but heartache crushes the spirit.

Psalm 55:22
Cast your cares on the Lord and he will sustain you; he will never let the righteous be shaken.

Psalm 34:18
The Lord is close to the brokenhearted and saves those who are crushed in spirit.

John 14:27
Peace I leave with you; my peace I give to you. I do not give to you as the world gives. Do not let your hearts be troubled, and do not be afraid.

Proverbs 17:22
A joyful heart is good medicine, but a broken spirit dries up the bones.

Philippians 4:13
I can do all this through him who gives me strength.

Session 2

The Struggle

Doubt and Unbelief Are Ambushes

Objectives

As a result of exploring **Doubt and Unbelief Are Ambushes**, you will learn to…

> ➤ recognize doubt and unbelief as thieves designed to steal, kill, and destroy the power of your faith—keeping you in the status quo community
> ➤ understand how these twins attack your thoughts daily to undermine your authority and render you powerless over circumstances
> ➤ notice when you are giving way to doubt and unbelief rather than trusting God's Word

1. Doubt and unbelief are identified as sneaky twins. Consider situations in your life when you found it difficult to trust God as a loving Father and see yourself as His beloved son/daughter. How did doubt and unbelief play a role here?

2. When we struggle to take God at His Word, we give room in our heart to be seduced by the culture of the world we live in rather than being influenced by the kingdom we come from. Consider your thoughts about money, wealth, status, and possessions. In what way has doubt and unbelief, in the faithfulness of God, shaped your outlook towards these things?

3. This chapter discusses how several symptoms of doubt and unbelief may manifest in our lives—rendering our heart unable to see the hope God offers. Check those that are a struggle for you. Feel free to insert others that may apply to you.

_____ Worry
_____ Anxiety
_____ Control
_____ Self-sabotage
_____ Over-achieving
_____ Anger
_____ Fear
_____ Depression
_____ Hopelessness

        _____
        _____
        _____

4. How have these struggles affected your ability to live a life surrounded by peace and joy?

5. Look up and write out the following scriptures. What does each one tell you about doubt and unbelief? Add to your Bible deck those which strengthen you.

Romans 4:20

Mark 9:23-24

Matthew 14:30-31

Mark 11:23

2 Corinthians 5:7

Luke 24:37-38

Session 2

The Struggle

Battle Fatigue Is Real
Objectives

As a result of exploring **Battle Fatigue Is Real**, you will learn to…

➤ understand you were born into an intense spiritual war zone
➤ discover the keys to overcome battle fatigue
➤ identify areas of your life where you're resisting God—knowingly or unintentionally

1. In this chapter we explore the fact that Satan wages war on the earth with a sole mission to steal, kill, and destroy. What areas of your life have you lost ground to the enemy? Relationships? Work? Family? Health? Finances? Dreams? Identifying these areas is the first step to recognizing where the enemy has targeted your life. List them here.

2. Have you been hurt in the battle? Are you tired and weary from the fight? Consider for a moment if you have been fighting the wrong enemy. What is God revealing to you about these battles?

3. Now, understanding that the enemy's goal is to wear you out, and God's plans are to give you the victory, write a statement telling God you trust Him as your commander in chief. Express your willingness to pick up your spiritual weapons and fight according to His directions.

4. On pages 22 and 23 we read the references of the Biblical accounts at the Red Sea, the walls of Jericho, the fiery pit, the lion's den, Sarah's barren womb, and the giant named Goliath. Take a moment and read through these stories for additional encouragement. The scripture references are listed below. For each verse, identify the struggle and the outcome. Choose those that encourage you the most and add them to your Bible deck.

Exodus 14:21-31

Joshua 6:1-16

Daniel 3:19-27

Daniel 6:16-23

Romans 4:18-20

1 Samuel 17: 20-50

What things will you bring to God in prayer? Reflect and write your prayer on the following page.

Reflection Page

Session 3

The Shift

A Heart Surrendered
A Mind Renewed
An Eternal Perspective

Recommended Reading
Strategic Faith Book, chapters 5-7

Session 3

The Shift

A Heart Surrendered

Objectives

As a result of exploring **A Heart Surrendered**, you will learn to…

➢ understand the importance of making a heart commitment to God
➢ see God existing beyond any boundaries
➢ develop a lifestyle of authentic surrender to God

1. This chapter challenges us to dig deep into the foundations of our belief system. The essence of overcoming our struggles lies in our understanding of who God is and how He operates. Here is where we begin to focus within. What does living a life connected to God mean to you?

2. On page 28 we read about how God called out the religious leaders of His time saying, *These people honor me with their lips, but their hearts are far from me. They worship me in vain; their teachings are merely human rules.* What do you think Jesus was implying here? Describe the dilemma the religious leaders found themselves in. Can you relate?

3. On page 29 we see the scripture passage from Psalm 139:1-4 which states that God knows everything about us. He knows our thoughts, our coming and going; He even knows the words we are going to speak before we speak them. This is a profound message. Have you ever considered the fact that God knows you this intimately? Write down your thoughts about this truth.

4. The Shift emphasizes the necessity of aligning our thinking with the truth of God's character and considering His Word as the ultimate measuring stick for our life. Is there anything in your perception of who God is that would cause you to doubt His trustworthiness?

5. In what ways do you use God's Word as a filter for your lifestyle?

6. In this chapter there are two thoughtful questions which require you to evaluate your relationship with God.

    ➢ Are you far from home today?

    ➢ What's keeping you from confidently running into the loving arms of your Father?

7. **John 15:5** "I am the vine; you are the branches. If you remain in me and I in you, you will bear much fruit; apart from me you can do nothing." Write in your own words how you apply this to your everyday life. Add this passage to your Bible deck.

Session 3

The Shift

A Mind Renewed

Objectives

As a result of exploring **A Mind Renewed**, you will learn to…

➤ develop a mindset focused on God's Word as the ultimate authority
➤ recognize thoughts as seeds which reap a harvest in your life
➤ establish a powerful thought life aimed at propelling you into your greatness

1. The mind is the battleground for most of our struggles. In this chapter, we learn much about the importance of recognizing the thoughts we allow to occupy space in our minds. Do you struggle with negative thoughts? How do these thoughts impact your daily life?

2. List any specific areas you are struggling with in your mind such as; unworthiness, shame, guilt, fear of the unknown, or any other disempowering thoughts. In identifying these you break the power they have to control you. Ask God to show you His thoughts regarding these areas—write down what you sense He is saying to you.

3. We have learned that our negative thoughts usually follow a pattern. Can you identify specific times when you struggle with your thoughts the most? Give this some consideration and write down what you uncover. This will help you to become aware of opportune times the enemy targets your mind so you can dismiss any self-destructive thoughts quickly.

4. Where is it necessary to make a shift in your thinking and speech in order to see the outcome you desire? Begin to make a list of those things. Write out a declaration prayer stating what God's truth is regarding your particular situation—even if you don't see it that way now. Use the examples on page 36 and 37 as a guide.

5. Living beyond limitations requires us to work hard at our thought life, consequently, effecting our speech and actions. We don't have to entertain every thought that comes our way. Does this truth empower you? Make a declaration statement expressing authority over your thoughts and speech.

Session 3

The Shift

An Eternal Perspective

Objectives

As a result of exploring **An Eternal Perspective**, you will learn to…

> ➤ shift your heart away from the here and now to the much larger canvas of eternity
> ➤ see your life through God's perspective and evaluate your priorities
> ➤ understand your life has a divine purpose to which you are responsible

1. Living by faith will confuse your mind at every turn. By faith we are to keep our eyes fixed on what is unseen—recognizing the world around us is temporary. Ask the Holy Spirit to reveal to you any limiting beliefs that are preventing you from embracing a life led by faith and not by sight.

2. Without an eternal perspective it is easy to be distracted with the cares of the world. What things or experiences may be hindering you from embracing your everyday life with an eternal perspective?

3. We read an important warning in this chapter; in the absence of an eternal perspective we can auto-cruise through life without a true sense of purpose. Stop and take a moment to ask God which of your habitual routines are preventing you from seeing Him at work around you? Write down what He says. How will this awareness cause you to make shifts in your daily habits?

4. Seeing life through a spiritual lens changes everything. What things/people in your life do you need to see through the lens of God's eyes? What/who is God bringing to mind? A good indicator is anything or anyone that you feel *rubs you the wrong way*. List them here. Ask God to show you what He sees. How does this change your focus?

5. On page 41 there are five questions to help you develop a strategic perspective. How would you answer these questions?

   ➢ What is the standard measuring stick for your life?

   ➢ Have you chosen to follow God with your whole heart?

> ➢ Do you live for today without concern for tomorrow?

> ➢ Is God in the forefront of your consciousness or only in a compartment of your life?

> ➢ What is holding you back from making the necessary shift to unleash life-transforming faith in your everyday life?

4. What is your favorite take away from this chapter?

5. **2 Corinthians 4:18** helps us to have an eternal perspective. *So we fix our eyes not on what is seen, but on what is unseen since what is seen is temporary, but what is unseen is eternal.* Add this to your Bible deck.

What things will you bring to God in prayer? Reflect and write your prayer on the following page.

Reflection Page

Session 4

The Strategy
Steps One & Two

Drink from the Well
Live to Love

Recommended Reading
Strategic Faith Book, chapters 8-9

Session 4

The Strategy

Step One: Drink from the Well
Objectives

As a result of exploring **Drink from the Well**, you will learn to…

➤ become anchored in your true identity
➤ embrace your God-given authority
➤ recognize you have a divine purpose

Now is the time when you will take the action steps to move into God's strategic plans for your life. God's divine purpose is for you to live beyond any earthy limitations. Proceed through the questions intentionally listening for the guidance of the Holy Spirit.

1. This chapter opens up with a great question—Who are you? Take a moment and honestly, and without judgment, reflect on how you perceive yourself today. The good, the bad, and the ugly are acceptable here. (Later we will combat any lies that you may believe about yourself.)

2. We have learned that drinking from a polluted well is the enemy's way of stealing your identity. It's time to make the decision to drink from the well that Jesus supplies. Make a list of those things that have polluted your self-image and altered the perception of your true identity. Decide today to allow God to tenderly speak His truths to your heart. What do you hear Him saying to you?

3. After reading about authority on pages 48-53 explain why it is important for you to walk in the fullness of who you are and the authority given to you by God.

4. Can you relate in any way to the story of the woman at the well? What things have ambushed you from seeing your true value? How has this played a role in your interactions with others?

5. It's time to put into action what you have learned about your true identity. Write a note to yourself—describe what makes you unique and valuable. Be specific. Go ahead—don't be shy. God knows it already; it's time you take ownership of it. Your impression of yourself is what you will project towards others. Store this letter in a convenient place so you can refer to it anytime the enemy wants to tell you that you are not worthy or that you are powerless.

6. Below are Bible verses that speak to your identity in Christ. Look these up and write them out. Add any favorites to your Bible deck.

2 Corinthians 5:17

Genesis 1:27

Jeremiah 1:5a

1 Peter 2:9

Galatians 2:20

7. Read the declaration prayer on page 53. Listen to hear what God is highlighting to you. Make your notes on the following page.

Notes

Session 4

The Strategy

Step Two: Live to Love

Objectives

As a result of exploring **Live to Love**, you will learn to…

- ➢ understand what true love is
- ➢ receive the unconditional love of God as Father
- ➢ allow God's love to transform your heart
- ➢ share God's love with others unconditionally

1. How do you define love? What do you think shaped your outlook?

2. The author shared that her religious upbringing made it difficult for her to see God as a loving Father. What has been your experience? Is there anything preventing you from seeing God as a loving Father?

3. Because we are made in God's image, we have the ability to love like God does—unconditionally. Is this difficult for you do to? Why or why not?

4. At times we are unaware of the many ways God demonstrates His love towards us every day. Be still and ask God to show you where you have missed His loving attempts to get your attention. Don't dismiss anything you hear. You may be surprised at what He shows you. Write about this here.

5. We have learned, contrary to popular cultural beliefs, love is not a feeling—it's a decision. This decision starts with us. We cannot give away what we don't have. First, we must accept God's love towards us and then we must decide to love ourselves despite our imperfections. This allows us to extend pure love towards others. Take time and write yourself a love letter. Write as if you were expressing devotion to someone you deeply cared about. As you engage in this assignment, allow God's love to cover you and wash away any feelings that do not speak into your greatness. **(Be encouraged to write this in a journal or someplace where you can reference it in the future, you will want to come back to this.)**

6. Was the above assignment difficult to do? Why or why not?

7. In this chapter, we learn how God's love, working through us, is independent upon our lives being perfect. Have you ever allowed the messes in your life to disqualify you from sharing God's love with others? Acknowledge these areas now. Write them down so you can surrender them to God and recommit to living in love regardless of the circumstances surrounding you.

8. In this life we often stumble across people who are difficult to love. Can you think of anyone? Remembering that you are created to be a vessel of God's love, ask the Holy Spirit to give you creative ideas of how you can reach out and be a blessing to this person(s). Write it down and commit to taking action.

9. Look up **Matthew 22:37-39**. Add this verse to your Bible deck.

10. Read the declaration prayer on pages 61-62. Listen to hear what God is highlighting to you. Make your notes on the following page.

Notes

Session 5

The Strategy
Steps Three & Four

Who Told You That?
Forgiveness Is the Way Forward—part 1

Recommended Reading
Strategic Faith Book, chapters 10-11 (pages 63-88)

The Strategy

Step Three: Who Told You That?

Objectives

As a result of exploring **Who Told You That**? You will learn to…

➤ recognize the noisy world designed to derail you from your created greatness
➤ develop a strategy to decipher which voices warrant your attention
➤ dispel lies that oppose truth
➤ sharpen your senses to the world of the spirit and the voice of God
➤ trust beyond your own understanding

1. It is imperative that we understand the reality that there exists an enemy whose schemes are designed to distract us from living in our created greatness. This was evident back in the Garden of Eden—it's still true today. Can you identify any areas of your life where you have taken the bait and believed something about God, His Word, or yourself, that wasn't true? How has this impacted your life?

2. We read in this chapter that God's commands will never give way to the ever-changing cultural trends. Consequently, we being citizens of heaven, can often find ourselves in a tug-of-war with what society condones and what God condemns. When this happens, do you feel the pressure of society to conform to its standards? How do you respond? Supply an example.

3. On pages 67- 69, the author shares of her struggles with fear, doubt, insecurity, and inadequacy. She gave us her go-to-list of truths that she uses to resist the enemy and shift her thinking. Look this list over and write down any of the truths that you find helpful in dealing with your personal struggles. Commit these to memory so you are armed and ready for battle the next time the enemy pulls up to your house and rings your doorbell.

4. David was a great warrior. He wasn't trained in the armed forces, but rather on the battlefield of life–alone and tired. Nonetheless, his everyday struggles prepared him for the greatness God had planned for him. Look back at what you consider to be a difficult season in your life. Can you now see how God was strengthening you, teaching you, and building your character? Write down what you uncover.

5. Are you creating limitations in your life because of the voices you are paying attention to? Where is the noise opting for your attention coming from? TV, podcasts, books, music, or perhaps the people you are hanging around? Ask God to highlight any areas you need to pay attention to. Write down what He shows you and commit to silencing these limiting voices.

6. Be certain—God who has begun a good work in you will see it through to completion. Write out **Philippians 1:6** and add it to your Bible deck.

7. Read the declaration prayer on page 77. Listen to hear what God is highlighting to you. Make your notes on the following page.

Notes

Session 5

The Strategy

Step Four: Forgiveness Is the Way Forward—part 1

Objectives

As a result of exploring **Forgiveness Is the Way Forward—part 1**, you will learn to...

- ➤ understand the power of forgiveness
- ➤ see God as the righteous judge
- ➤ trust your internal GPS system

This chapter explores a very sensitive subject—forgiveness. As you proceed through this section be honest and patient with yourself. Don't judge where you are currently; keep your eyes on where God is taking you—to a life beyond limitations.

1. Jesus lovingly instructs us to engage the strategy of forgiveness so we can undermine the schemes of the enemy. Walking down the pathway of forgiveness is a foreign concept in our culture. After all, we have been conditioned to protect ourselves from being hurt at all cost. Yet, Jesus instructs us differently. Write about any struggles you are facing in your own mind as you choose to embrace this strategy as a necessary step to a life beyond limitations.

2. Forgiveness has everything to do with trusting God. We are instructed to forgive and embrace God's promise to make things right in His timing and in His way. Examine your heart. Ask yourself if you are truly willing to forgive and trust the outcome to God? Write about your thoughts.

3. Jesus' response to those who pointed their fingers at the woman who was caught in adultery surprised everyone. To what degree does His response cause you to reflect and consider what is underlying your justification to withhold grace towards the misdeeds of others?

4. Forgiveness is the key to unlock the vault of pain in your heart. It empowers you to live above the limitations of your feelings. Examining the vaults you have created within your heart, and deciding to allow God access, is the key to the peace you have been longing for. Who do you need to forgive? What offense(s) are keeping you in bondage?

5. Become an agent of debt forgiveness cancellation (page 83). Look at your list above. What needs to happen in order to activate forgiveness in these areas?

6. Your internal GPS will always direct you towards forgiveness. Your feelings will always lead you in the opposite direction. When your GPS guides you to forgive—choose to quickly obey. Below are a few scriptures to remind you that forgiveness is the way forward. Which ones empower you the most? Add those to your Bible deck. Add others that you uncover.

Ephesians 4:32
Be kind and compassionate to one another, forgiving each other, just as in Christ God forgave you.

Colossians 3:13
Bear with each other and forgive one another if any of you has a grievance against someone. Forgive as the Lord forgave you.

Romans 12:19
Do not take revenge, my dear friends, but leave room for God's wrath, for it is written; "It is mine to avenge; I will repay," says the Lord.

1 Peter 3:9
Do not repay evil for evil or insult with insult. On the contrary, repay evil with blessing, because to this you were called so that you may inherit a blessing.

Look back over what you have studied this week. What things will you bring to God in prayer?

Session 6

The Strategy
Steps Four & Five

Forgiveness Is the Way Forward—part 2
It's a New Day

Recommended Reading
Strategic Faith Book, chapters 11-12 (pages 88-106)

Session 6

The Strategy

Step Four: Forgiveness Is the Way Forward—part 2
Objectives

As a result of exploring **Forgiveness Is the Way Forward—part 2**, you will learn to...

➤ embrace the power of the grace card
➤ understand God's character and come to realize He is not the author of evil
➤ make peace with the unexplainable happening in life

> *Part 2 is difficult for many people. If this is you—know you are not alone. Take as much time as you need to fully grasp the loving nature of God. If necessary, pray and ask the Holy Spirit to help you see past any hurt and pain which may be causing you to see yourself or God through an obscured lens.*

1. We can grow into a place of forgiving others and forget to offer the same grace to ourselves. Is it difficult for you to forgive yourself of the mistakes you have made and the hurt you may have caused others? Explain.

2. Give yourself permission to write out things you may still be charging yourself guilty of and offer yourself the grace card.

3. Embracing the strategy of self-forgiveness empowers you to live your life to the fullest. Explain how this truth has impacted you.

4. Are there any specific situations in your life where you would say, "I blame God for _____, or I don't understand why God allowed _____ to happen"? (Fill in the blanks if applicable) It's okay—God isn't angry. He understands and desires that the truth of His love will set you free. Talk to Him about these situations and listen for what He is saying to you. Write about that conversation here.

5. After reading this chapter, can you make the shift in your heart to believe God can be trusted even when you don't understand the why surrounding circumstance? Why or why not?

6. On page 94 we read another bold statement, *Settle once and for all that God is not, and cannot, be the author of evil.* Do you struggle with reconciling this truth in your own heart? Write down your thoughts, struggles, and feelings. Don't discount them—they are all part of the process of releasing the pain and uncovering the truth about God's character.

7. How would your life be different if you only saw God through the lens of His perfect love for humanity regardless of what circumstances were presented before you?

8. Arm yourself with the power that will destroy the lies opposing the loving character of God. Below are several scriptures aimed to give you the ammunition you need. Add to your Bible deck those which are most helpful.

1 John 1:5b
God is light; in him there is no darkness at all.

Psalm 18:30
As for God, his way is perfect; the Lord's Word is flawless; he shields all who take refuge in him.

Psalm 23:4

Even though I walk through the darkest valley, I will fear no evil, for you are with me, your rod and your staff, they comfort me.

Psalm 121:3

He will not let your foot slip—he who watches over you will not slumber.

9.   Read the declaration prayer on pages 94-95. Listen to hear what God is highlighting to you. Make your notes on the following page.

Notes

Session 6

The Strategy

Step Five: It's a New Day

Objectives

As a result of exploring **It's a New Day**, you will learn to…

> ➤ trust God in the midst of change
> ➤ release old thought patterns and habits that are cluttering your closet
> ➤ persevere until you cross the finish line
> ➤ embrace every day with a sense of excitement and expectation

1. Nature doesn't argue with its creator—a valuable lesson for us humans to embrace. How do you handle change? Do you yield to the shifting tides or find yourself resisting? What thoughts flood your mind when you're facing change in your life?

2. Holding tightly to the things you should be letting go of renders you unequipped to enter the new seasons ahead. It's time to do a deep cleaning. What thoughts, habits, and relationships are stinking up your closet?

3. Living out your created greatness means learning to strategize against defeat. Page 102 list training tools to help you develop this discipline, (**Regroup, Pray, Review, Believe, Trust**). Look these over and consider how each one would be beneficial to you. What steps can you put into place to ensure these become your go-to gear when needed?

4. Learning that life is a marathon—not a sprint, and comparison is a trap designed to distract you—what changes do you need to make to stay in your own lane and endure the race?

5. Greatness is never birthed in the comfort zone. It takes courage to break away from the status quo. In this chapter you have learned six principles to help you persevere when everything around you is resisting the change of the new day. Which of these do you need to incorporate in your everyday life? Are there any that you have already mastered? (Refer to pages 104-105)

6. Below are a few scriptures to remind you that trusting in the Lord every day, and in all seasons of life, provides peace. Which scriptures empower you the most? Add them to your Bible deck.

Proverbs 3:5-6
Trust in the Lord with all your heart and lean not on your own understanding; in all your ways submit to him, and he will make your paths straight.

Psalm 46:10
Be still and know that I am God; I will be exalted among the nations, I will be exalted in the earth.

Jeremiah 29:11
For I know the plans I have for you, declares the Lord, plans to prosper you and not to harm you, plans to give you hope and a future.

Isaiah 41:10
So do not fear, for I am with you; do not be dismayed, for I am your God. I will strengthen you and help you; I will uphold you with my righteous right hand.

Philippians 4:6-7
Do not be anxious about anything, but in every situation, by prayer and petition, with thanksgiving, present your requests to God. And the peace of God, which transcends all understanding, will guard your hearts and your minds in Christ Jesus.

7.   Read the declaration prayer on pages 105-106. Listen to hear what God is highlighting to you. Make your notes on the following page.

Notes

Session 7

The Strategy
Steps Six & Seven

Rest Is a Weapon
Dreaming beyond Limits

Recommended Reading
Strategic Faith Book, chapters 13-14

Session 7

The Strategy

Step Six: Rest Is a Weapon

Objectives

As a result of exploring **Rest Is a Weapon**, you will learn to…

➢ understand God's perspective on rest
➢ strategically position yourself to use rest as a weapon
➢ listen for God's commands before engaging in battle
➢ avoid the war zone at all cost

1. On page 109 we learn what rest means in God's kingdom. It's a crucial part of the plan for victory and requires relentless faith. The expression *let go and let God* makes sense, but it's especially hard to do for those who prefer to be in control. What are some things you do that get in the way of relinquishing control to God? What will you do to cooperate rather than control?

2. Living strategically according to God's plan requires relentless faith—a faith that understands resting in God is a place of safety. In this chapter, five strategies are discussed which, when ignited with faith, will propel you into God's rest. Reflect and identify which ones present a struggle for you. Next, consider what action steps you can take to begin to implement these in your everyday life. Write down your action steps.

    ➤ Embrace the present
    ➤ Don't be in a hurry
    ➤ See the beauty in all things
    ➤ Be thankful
    ➤ Give yourself the *grace* card

3. When you consider using rest as a weapon against the schemes of the enemy what limiting thoughts and habits are holding you back?

4. Being at rest in God requires a new perspective. You have a choice. You can stay in a state of frenzy, or you can choose to leave self-defeating mindsets behind and run confidently into God's loving arms. This chapter identifies a process for running into God's arms:

Stop ⇒ Breathe ⇒ Praise God ⇒ Meditate on God's love for you

Try this right now. How does that feel? (Write that down.) How long did that take? Rest is your secret weapon. Make this a daily tool for your strategic faith journey! Write yourself this reminder… **Stop. Breathe. Praise. Meditate.** Place it where you will see it often.

5. Understanding that you are in a tug of war with your old sin nature (your thoughts and habits that do not align with the truth of who you are, the power you possess, or the purpose for which you were created), and your new nature (being fashioned every day into your original design), can leave you weary in the struggle. What action step(s) can you take that would be a constant reminder that you are a work in progress? Be creative.

6. Look up the following Bible verses and add any passages that encourage you to trust and rest in God's faithfulness to your Bible deck.

Hebrews 4:1

Matthew 11:28-29

Psalm 91:1-2

Numbers 23:19

7. Read the declaration prayer on page 118. Now read it again. Listen to hear what God is highlighting to you. Make your notes on the following page.

Notes

The Strategy

Step Seven: Dreaming beyond Limits
Objectives

As a result of exploring **Dreaming beyond Limits**, you will learn to…

- ➢ recognize who is behind the helm steering the ship of your life
- ➢ uncover if you are stuck in a dream which is outside of your created purpose
- ➢ crush limiting beliefs
- ➢ dream with God

> *This chapter challenges you to recognize who is at the helm of your life—you or God. Now is the time to uncover the answer. The following questions are designed to help get a clear picture of the habits you have become accustomed to—those things which are navigating the course of your life and may be drifting you away from the greatness God intended for you.*

1. This chapter opens with five reflection points. Honestly reply as the Holy Spirit reveals what He wants you to see.

➤ What part of your daily routine is set to autopilot—going through the motions with no sense of deep satisfaction?

➤ What is the driving force behind your decision-making?

➤ How are you allowing yourself to be influenced by the expectations of others?

➤ What goals are you pursuing that no longer fit who you are today?

➤ In what way is your life drastically different than what you dreamed it would be, leaving you feeling frustrated and stuck? Or perhaps, is your life exactly what you dreamed about—only to find yourself empty inside?

2. Looking back, can you now recognize times when you have made decisions that pulled you away from the greatness you were created for? What shifts do you need to make to ensure this does not continue to reoccur in your life?

3. Do you hear the alarm sounding—have you settled for the status quo life? In what ways have you allowed your life to become comfortable—not willing to take the risk even though everything within you is saying—JUMP? Ask God. Write what you are hearing.

4. Below are three action steps that will activate your faith to believe you can dream big with God. The degree to which you are desperate to live a life beyond limitations is the degree to which you will fight to implement God's strategies in your life. In which of these areas does your faith need to be strengthened? Write down what God is showing you.

> **Push**—through the pain in the midst of the battle
> **Trust**—God in the darkness of despair
> **Achieve**—more than you dreamed possible

5. Re-read pages 126-131, *Prayer is Essential.* God's purpose for your life extends far beyond yourself and your immediate needs. This is an eye-opening revelation. Given this knowledge, what do you have in your hands *right now* that God can easily multiply for the greater good? How can you partner with God? Think outside of the box. Write down your thoughts—you may be surprised at what comes to mind.

6. Commitment is necessary to fulfill all that God has planned for you. Behind every great dreamer you will find a life etched with commitment. What shifts do you need to make to give yourself permission to seeing God-size dreams come to pass in your life?

7. In what ways do you imagine your life being different if you gave yourself permission to dream beyond limits?

8.   Review the Bible verses below and add to your Bible deck those most relevant to you.

Philippians 4:13 [AMP]

I can do all things {which He has called me to do} through Him who strengthens and empowers me {to fulfill His purpose—I am self-sufficient in Christ's sufficiency; I am ready for anything and equal to anything through Him who infuses me with inner strength and confident peace.}

Isaiah 41:10

So do not fear, for I am with you; do not be dismayed, for I am your God. I will strengthen you and help you; I will uphold you with my righteous right hand.

Jeremiah 29:11

For I know the plans I have for you, declares the Lord, plans to prosper you and not to harm you, plans to give you hope and a future.

Psalms 32:8

I will instruct you and teach you in the way you should go; I will counsel you with my loving eye on you.

9.   Read the declaration prayer on pages 136-137. Listen to hear what God is highlighting to you. Look back over what you have studied this week and determine what you will bring to God in prayer? Make these notes on the following page.

Notes

Session 8

Your Strategic Faith Journey

No More Excuses

Recommended Reading
Strategic Faith Book, chapter 15

Session 8

Your Strategic Faith Journey

No More Excuses

Objectives

As a result of exploring **No More Excuses**, you will learn...

➢ you are irreplaceable
➢ you can live confidently in your God-given identity
➢ you have the power to stand boldly in your authority
➢ your life is a part of God's divine plan for such a time as this
➢ it is your responsibility to take your position in God's kingdom to impact and influence your family, community, and the world

Reading through each page of Strategic Faith and completing the exercises in this workbook has placed you on a personal faith development journey with God. He is teaching you and preparing you to strategically use your faith to live beyond limitations. It is not by accident that you have been on this adventure. God has a plan and purpose for equipping you. No longer can you live in the status quo community—you know and understand too much about God's kingdom principles to settle for anything less than His greatness manifesting in your life—No More Excuses!

1. God is consumed with purpose not perfection. It's now time for you to throw away any limiting excuses holding you back from living in your created greatness. Review the objectives for this chapter and write a declaration statement personalizing each one. Elaborate in anyway necessary to solidify these truths in your heart.

Declaration statement

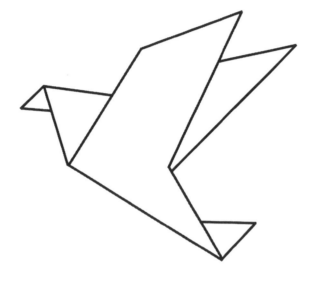

Next Steps

Be an ambassador of change

Below is a list of ways you can get involved and become an ambassador of change—empowering others to live in their created greatness. Yes—you! Pray and see how God is leading you.

➢ **Step out in faith**—Share the Strategic Faith book and workbook with others you know or come in contact with—family members, friends, neighbors, co-workers, church members and leaders. Give God an opportunity to work in their lives just as He did in yours. Sharing is caring.

➢ **Discipleship**—You can help strengthen or guide someone else along their faith development journey. You have all the tools you need. You've read the book and done the workbook exercises. You are more than capable to invite someone you know to read and go through the workbook with you as a mentor.

➢ **Lead a group**—Gather several people together to walk this journey side by side. Imagine the impact you can make as you share your faith development journey and encourage others along their pathway to greatness. Consider friends, family, co-workers, or church family. Everyone has room to grow, and you can be the spark they need to become an ambassador of change for God's glory.

If you need extra support, be sure to connect and engage in the Facebook group (Strategic Ambassadors). You can also reach out to Lucy Ann; her contact information is listed below. Be an influential strategic ambassador. Help others to live in their created greatness—A Life Beyond Limitations.

Website: LucyAnnCQ.com
Facebook: Strategic Ambassadors or Lucy Ann Coasta-Quattrone Coach
Instagram: LucyAnnCQ
Email: LucyAnnCQ@gmail.com

StayEmpowered

> ➢ Be committed to living strategically by faith—every day.
> ➢ Review your Bible deck regularly and add to it continually.
> ➢ Stay in community with like-minded believers and encourage one another to impact earth with the fullness of God's kingdom.

If you personally want to take your faith to another level, dig deeper into your God-given identity, authority, and purpose, so that you can live in your created greatness—join
Lucy Ann's coaching program.

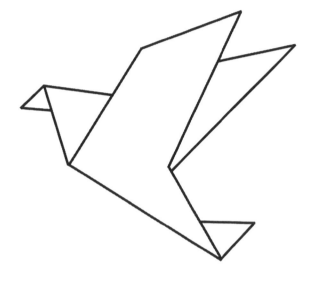

Bonuses

Declaration prayers for easy reference

Drink from the Well

Declaration Prayer

I belong to my heavenly Father who loves me unconditionally. Thank you, Father, for creating me with unique gifts and talents to fulfill your divine plans for my life. I cast down any self-image that does not align with who you say I am, and receive my rightful place as your son/daughter. I am not an orphan, an accident, or insignificant in any way; I am your child. I stand righteous in your sight. I am holy and sanctified not by my own merit but through the sacrifice Jesus made on the cross for my redemption. I choose to drink only from the well of living water.

My significance is found in my relationship with my heavenly Father; nothing and no one can change this truth. Forevermore, I shall see my reflection through the mirror of God's love. I stand confidently in my God-given identity and authority. I stand boldly against any attack of the enemy with confidence that I have the victory. No one else can be me and I do not desire to be anyone else. I am irreplaceable. Amen.

Live to Love

Declaration Prayer

Heavenly Father, I am thankful for the greatest gift of all—your love. I open my heart to receive all the love you have for me. Your love covers my sins through the blood of Jesus and not by any works of my own doing. I commit to loving and trusting you with my whole heart.

Holy Spirit, thank you for helping me to see others and myself through the eyes of the Father's love. I receive your empowerment to love even when my thoughts and feelings are tugging me in another direction. I will choose love over hate every day. When my life seems messy, I will continue to trust in God's plans and purposes for each day, and I will choose to seek that out. I shall be an instrument of your love.

I stand boldly with my heart fixed on you and turn away from the lust of the world. Your love shining through me will brighten the atmosphere wherever I go. Amen.

Who Told You That?

Declaration Prayer

Father, thank you for your Word—a love letter to me. I declare that I shall pay attention to what you say. I will not let your words out of my sight; I will keep them within my heart. They are life to me and health to my whole body. I will guard my heart and keep it pure before you. I will keep my mouth free of perversity and corrupt talk.

My eyes are fixed on you as I give careful thought to the path I follow. I will be steadfast in all my ways. I will cast down every argument and every idea that sets itself up against the truth of who you are and what your Word declares to be true. I will stand steadfast in the face of any giant and call upon your name, lean on your strength, and uphold your ways.

Father, thank you for giving me the faith to stand strong in the face of any opponent; I will dispel the lies that oppose your Word, and I will stand confidently on your truth. I will listen for your voice and obey your commands. Amen.

Forgiveness Is the Way Forward

Declaration Prayer

Father God, thank you for showering me with your forgiveness. I stand righteous before you because of the blood of Jesus. You remember my sins no more. They are as far as the east is from the west. I choose to release all my shame, guilt, and feelings of unworthiness to you. My heart is wide open to live free of any condemnation—either self-imposed or otherwise—aimed towards me. I am free to live every day in your peace.

I choose to accept that your ways are not my ways. Forgiveness is a strategy from heaven that frees me from the bondage of hurts—past, present, and future. I choose to forgive others. I will not allow my heart to be deceived into thinking I have a right to hold offense against anyone. I cancel all debts of offense. Thank you for giving me eyes to see others the way you see them. I give you permission to administer justice according to your perfect will as I keep my heart fixed on you. I will love others through the power of your Holy Spirit. I bless my enemies. I will not allow the actions of others to knock me off the path of righteousness and derail my purpose.

You are a just God. I repent for holding you responsible for the things I cannot explain. I stand humbly before you, trusting in your unfailing love for me. Amen.

It's a New Day

Declaration Prayer

My history no longer speaks to my future. The pain and suffering that I've endured does not speak louder than my strength and courage. I now understand that God's presence is with me every day. I am eager to uncover the mysteries of each new day. I give myself permission to experiment with new things without the fear of failure. I see each day as a journey of discovery. Eagerly, and unashamedly, I will ask question after question in my search for wisdom. I will make the most of every opportunity to learn and explore. The confidence I display each day enables me to conquer task after task. Boldly I acknowledge my strengths—not waiting for or needing anyone else's approval. I have a built-in tenacity that grants me the courage to keep on trying, even in the face of defeat, and to conquer when all odds are against me. Each new day through my eyes is priceless. Amen.

Rest Is a Weapon

Declaration Prayer

Father God, I choose to cast aside worry, fear, and anxiety. I decree and declare that I will surrender control of my life into your faithful hands. I choose to rest in your unfailing love for me. I trust you with all that concerns me, from the smallest detail to the most important circumstances. I will use your strategy of rest to fight my battles. Your Word is my sword, my faith is my shield, and rest is my weapon. I trust you are with me, you go before me, and you always make a safe pathway for my feet to walk. I lay my burdens down and leave them with you. I trust everything and everyone who is dear to my heart into your loving care. Thank you there is no battle too great for you to gain the victory on my behalf. I receive rest as a strategic plan from heaven. Amen.

Dreaming beyond Limits

Heavenly Father, your creative genius is running through my DNA. I will, from this day forward, release my mind to dream beyond limits. There is nothing that is impossible with you. Though I may not clearly see the how or when, I know you are able to lead, guide, and direct my path according to your dreams for my life. I stand committed to do my part and obey as you instruct. I will stand in faith in the face of all opposition until every dream you place in my heart is fulfilled, and every mountain standing in the way is washed out to sea.

The enemy shudders when my feet hit the ground each day. I give myself permission to move in unison with your Spirit. I cast down any doubts, fears, cultural limitations, or religious beliefs that will hinder my ability to reach beyond the stars. I align my heart with your promises for my life. Use me to impact the world around me for your glory. Amen.

Acknowledgements

A Big shout out to my dear friend—Susan Bish, for her amazing insight and wisdom in helping me to complete this workbook with excellence. Susan, you are amazing. Thank you from the depths of my heart.

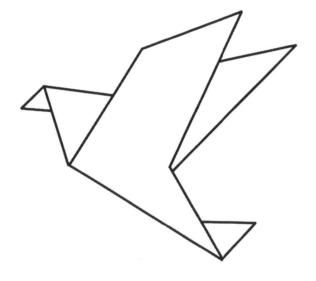

Leader's Guide

Leader's Guide

As a leader, please take note of the following key points as you guide others through this workbook. First and foremost, this workbook is not designed to be a Bible study—as some may be accustomed to. Rather, it's a book designed to lead others on a faith development journey into their created greatness.

This workbook is designed to invite all participants to dive deep into the struggles, shifts, and strategies, presented in the *Strategic Faith, Living Beyond Limitations* book. To get the full impact of the workbook it will take commitment and dedication to seeing the process through to the end.

Participants will be required to dig deep wells of honesty with themselves and with God as they move from struggle to strength and uncertainty to trust—this will be an amazing adventure.

Key leadership points to consider:

1. **Welcome everyone at every faith level.** This workbook is designed to cross all religious barriers and meet people at every stage of their faith journey— everyone has room to grow.

2. **Instruct and expect participants to share from the point of view of their personal faith experiences.** Allow no room for discussions which make generalizations regarding different faith practices. Everyone's experiences are theirs to explore and share as per those experiences. Everyone from all backgrounds of faith will be drawn to this book/workbook.

3. **Review, with your group, the points listed on page vi—how to use this workbook.** In doing so you will help everyone to keep these factors in mind as they progress through their faith development journey.

4. **Encourage everyone to share at the level at which they are comfortable**. Some topics may be too personal to share with others—instruct everyone to share according to their personal comfort level.

5. **Victory testimonies**. Some participants will have experienced victory in particular areas being discussed. Encourage these folks to share how they overcame obstacles and what they learned along the way. This will bring encouragement to others and be a beacon of light for what is possible.

6. **Prepare participants to have an open mind**. Participants will be challenged to explore what has influenced their beliefs system and attitudes on multiple levels.

7. **Encourage participants to do each assignment**. Doing the work presented will equip everyone to be strategically armed to live their everyday life as an ambassador of heaven—called to impact and influence earth with God's kingdom principles. They will learn to live from a place of newfound awareness of their God-given identity, authority, and purpose.

8. **You are a cheerleader**! As a leader you will be the cheerleader encouraging others to keep going when the road ahead seems tough, rough, and uncertain. Lead with conviction—no one quits on your watch. Get ready to see the impact of the kingdom of heaven inundate the hearts of everyone participating in this study.

9. **Pray**. Consistently pray for those you are leading. Ask God to open hearts and minds to receive revelation knowledge straight from His throne room to their spirits.

Meet the Author

To know Lucy Ann is to first and foremost recognize her deep devotion to God and her family. She is married to her incredible husband, Bryan, she's a mom and grandmother. She is passionate about living life to the fullest and helping others to do the same.

She loves to fly airplanes, ride motorcycles, surf, golf, hike, travel, and enjoy any adventure. When she is not exploring she loves to kick back with a great book. Her joy for life is contagious and overflows to everything she does.

After retiring as a commercial pilot and flight instructor she dedicated six years to work as a volunteer pastor in a military prison in California. It was behind the barbwire where she would say, "I learned the true meaning of God's love."

She now spends her time coaching, speaking, and writing. She is devoted to empowering others to partner with God, live by faith, and transform their lives to become powerful influencers in their homes, communities, and workplaces. Her dedication to the people she serves is undeniable.

Lucy Ann believes every person has value and purpose. You can read the many articles she has written on her blog, *Irreplaceable You*, found on her website. Her insightful thought process has afforded her the opportunity to write leadership training materials, and Bible study lessons to be used in small group settings, women's events, and leadership programs. Her book—*Strategic Faith, Living Beyond Limitations* won the Author's Elite first place award for its excellence in the writing and publishing industry in the non fiction category.

If you should cross her path in person, be forewarned, she loves capturing life through the lens of her camera and she is not shy about stopping anywhere, with anyone, at anytime, to take a picture. You may be in her next photo.

You can find out more about her services at LucyAnnCQ.com.

Made in the USA
Middletown, DE
15 August 2021